Camille
and the SUNFLOWERS

A story about **Vincent van Gogh**

by LAURENCE ANHOLT

FRANCES LINCOLN

WHERE Camille lived, the sunflowers
grew so high they looked like real suns -

LAURENCE ANHOLT is one of the UK's leading children's authors. He has written over 60 books which have been translated into 17 languages. His previous titles, in collaboration with his wife, Catherine, include *Catherine and Laurence Anholt's Big Book of Families* (Walker), *A Kiss Like This* (Hamish Hamilton) and *Billy and the Big New School* (Orchard).

Laurence has written and illustrated two other titles on lives of the artists: *Degas and the Little Dancer*: a story about Edgar Degas, and *Picasso and the Girl with a Ponytail*: a story about Pablo Picasso. His other titles for Frances Lincoln are *The Forgotten Forest* and *Can You Guess?* Laurence has three children and lives in a farmhouse by the sea in Lyme Regis.

Camille and the Sunflowers
© Frances Lincoln Limited 1994
Text and illustrations copyright
© Laurence Anholt 1994

First published in Great Britain in 1994 by
Frances Lincoln Limited, 4 Torriano Mews
Torriano Avenue, London NW5 2RZ

First paperback edition 1995

British Library Cataloguing in
Publication Data available on request

ISBN 0-7112-0900-6 hardback
ISBN 0-7112 1050-0 paperback

Printed in Hong Kong

5 7 9 8 6

The Postman Roulin (Collection: State
Museum Kröller-Müller, Otterlo, The
Netherlands); **La Berceuse** (Museum of Fine
Arts, Boston); **Armand Roulin** (Museum
Folkwang, Essen); **Roulin's Baby** (Chester Dale
Collection, National Gallery of Art, Washington);
Portrait of Camille Roulin (Museu de Arte
de São Paulo Assis Chateaubriand; photograph
by Luiz Hossaka); **Vase with 14 Sunflowers**
and **Self-portrait with Grey Felt Hat**
(Collection Vincent van Gogh Foundation/
Van Gogh Museum, Amsterdam).

For Cathy
With Love

a whole field of burning yellow suns.

Every day after school Camille
ran through the sunflowers to meet
his father, who was a postman.
Together they would lift down
the heavy sacks of mail.

One day a strange man arrived
in Camille's town. He had a straw
hat and a yellow beard. He looked
around with quick brown eyes.

"I am Vincent, the painter,"
he said, smiling at Camille.

Vincent moved into the yellow
house at the end of Camille's street.

He had no money and no friends.

"Let's try and help him," said Camille's father.

So they loaded up the postcart with pots and pans and old furniture for the yellow house.

Camille picked a huge bunch
of sunflowers for the painter and
put them in a big brown pot.

Vincent was very pleased to
have two good friends.

Vincent asked Camille's father if he
would like to have his picture painted,
dressed in his best blue uniform.

"You must sit quite still," said Vincent.

Camille watched everything. He loved
the bright colours Vincent used and the
strong smell of paint.

He saw the face of his father appear
like magic on the canvas.

The picture was strange but very beautiful.

Vincent said he would like
to paint the whole family -

Camille's mother,

his big brother,

his baby sister...

and at last, Camille himself.

Camille was very excited - he'd never
even had his photograph taken.

Camille took his painting into school.

He wanted everyone to see it.

But the children didn't like the picture.
They all began to laugh.

Then Camille felt very sad.

After school some of the older
children started teasing Vincent.

They ran along behind as he
went out to paint.

Even the grown-ups joined in.
"It's time he got a real job,"
they said, "instead of playing
with paints all day."

All that afternoon Camille sat watching
Vincent work. It was very hot but Vincent
worked fast. He painted the sunflower
fields and even the sun itself.

"He is the Sunflower Man," thought Camille.

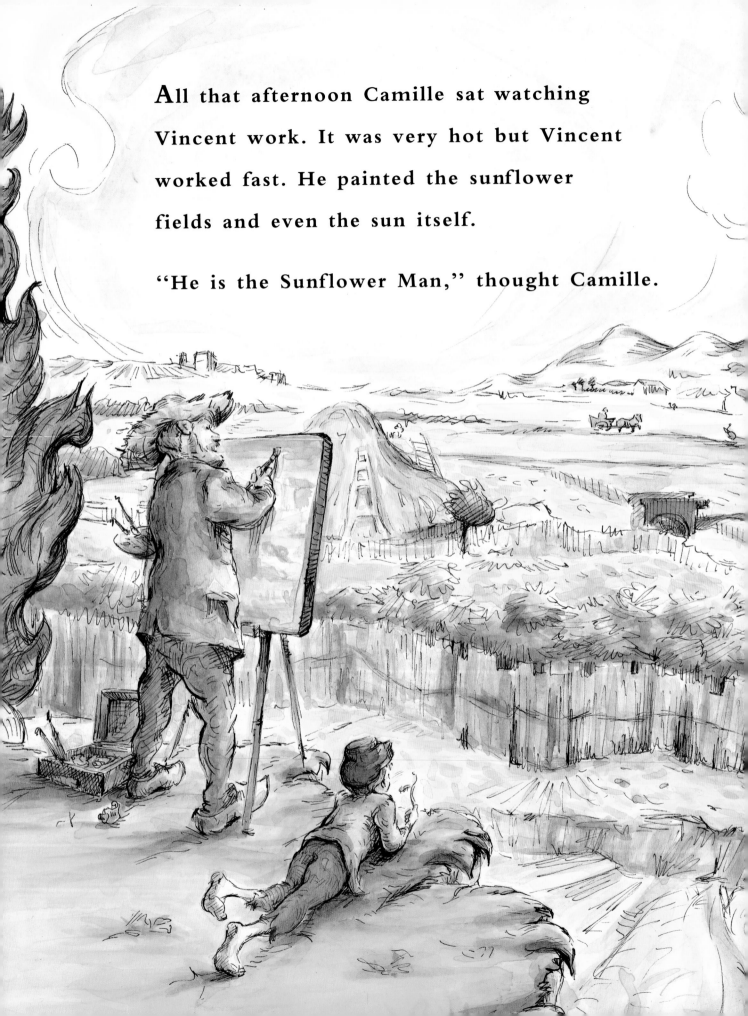

"If I were rich, I would buy all your paintings," he said.

"Thank you, my friend," laughed Vincent.

When Camille and Vincent came back
from the fields, some children from
Camille's school were waiting for them.

They shouted at Vincent and threw stones.

Camille wanted them to stop - but what
could he do? He was only a small boy.
At last he ran home in tears.

"Listen, Camille," said his father. "People often laugh at things that are different. But I've got a feeling that one day they will learn to love Vincent's paintings."

That night, Camille
had a strange dream.
He saw Vincent standing
in the moonlight
high above the town.

He had stuck candles on
his hat so that he could see.

The Sunflower Man
was painting the stars!

Early next morning, Camille was
woken by a loud knocking at the door.

Some men from the town had come
to see his father.

"Listen, Postman," they said.
"We want you to give this letter
to your friend. It says he must pack
up his paints and leave our town."

Camille slipped out through the back
door and ran down the street to
the yellow house.

It seemed very quiet inside.

Then Camille saw the sunflowers he had
picked for Vincent - they had all dried
up and died. Camille felt sadder than ever.

He found Vincent upstairs packing his bags.
Vincent looked very tired but he smiled
at Camille.

"Don't be sad," he said. "It's time
for me to paint somewhere else now.
Perhaps people there will like my pictures.

But first I have something to show you..."

Vincent lifted down a big picture.
There were Camille's sunflowers,
bigger and brighter than ever!

Camille looked at the painting.
Then he smiled, too.

"Goodbye, Sunflower Man,"
he whispered, and ran out of
the yellow house into the sunshine.

Camille's father was right. People did learn to love Vincent's paintings. Today you would have to be very rich to buy one. But people visit galleries and museums all over the world just to look at pictures of the yellow house, of Camille and his family, and most of all, the sunflowers - so bright and yellow they look like real suns.

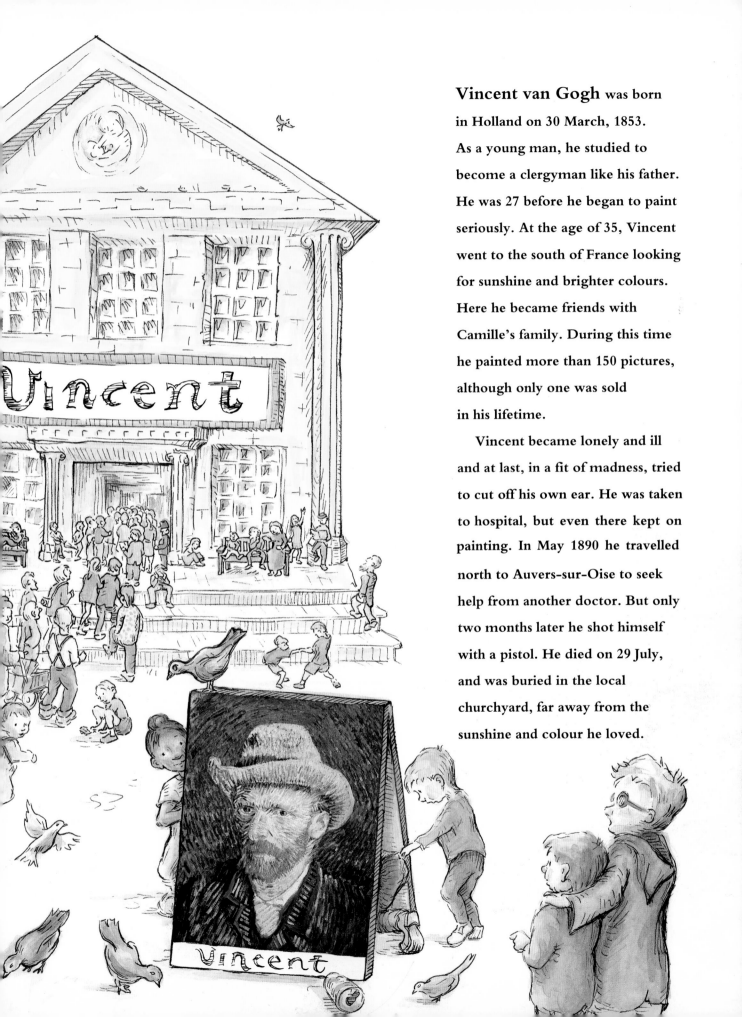

Vincent van Gogh was born in Holland on 30 March, 1853. As a young man, he studied to become a clergyman like his father. He was 27 before he began to paint seriously. At the age of 35, Vincent went to the south of France looking for sunshine and brighter colours. Here he became friends with Camille's family. During this time he painted more than 150 pictures, although only one was sold in his lifetime.

Vincent became lonely and ill and at last, in a fit of madness, tried to cut off his own ear. He was taken to hospital, but even there kept on painting. In May 1890 he travelled north to Auvers-sur-Oise to seek help from another doctor. But only two months later he shot himself with a pistol. He died on 29 July, and was buried in the local churchyard, far away from the sunshine and colour he loved.

MORE PICTURE BOOKS AVAILABLE FROM
FRANCES LINCOLN

PICASSO AND THE GIRL WITH A PONYTAIL
Laurence Anholt

Shy Sylvette dreams of becoming an artist, and when one day Picasso chooses her as his model, she begins to realise her dream. A highly accessible introduction to the life and work of Picasso.

Suitable for National Curriculum English – Reading, Key Stage 2; Art, Key Stage 2
Scottish Guidelines English Language, Reading, Levels B and C; Art and Design, Levels B and C

ISBN 0-7112-1176-0 **£9.99** (hb)

DEGAS AND THE LITTLE DANCER
Laurence Anholt

Marie wants to be a famous ballerina, so to find money for lessons, she begins modelling at the ballet school, for the artist, Edgar Degas. A charming introduction to the life of the great artist.

Suitable for National Curriculum Art, Key Stage 2; English – Reading, Key Stages 1 and 2
Scottish Guidelines Art and Design, Levels B and C; English Language – Reading, Levels B and C

ISBN 0-7112-1075-6 **£4.99**

MY STICKER ART GALLERY
Carole Armstrong

Solve the clues, and fill the frames of your own sticker art gallery with peelable mini-reproductions of paintings by some of the world's great artists!

Scottish Guidelines Art and Design, Levels B and C

ISBN 0-7112-0886-7 **£5.99**

Frances Lincoln titles are available from all good bookshops
Prices are correct at time of printing, but may be subject to change